ANNE GEDDES ™

TINY

Angels

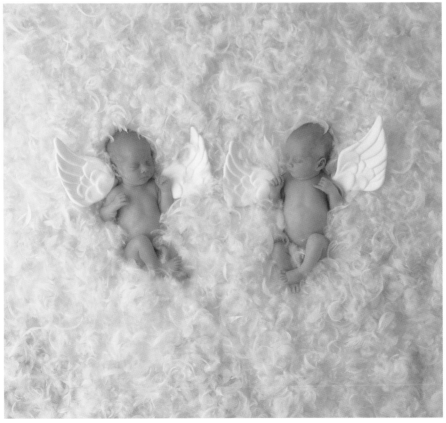

ISBN 1-55912-613-2

Please write to us for a FREE FULL COLOR CATALOG of our fine
Anne Geddes calendars and books, Cedco Publishing Company,
2955 Kerner Blvd., San Rafael, CA 94901.

The Anne Geddes 1998 Tiny Angels Datebook is owned and produced by
The Especially Kids Company Limited,
2 York Street, Parnell, Auckland, New Zealand.
Telephone 64-9-375 2566, Facsimile 64-9-375-2560

© Anne Geddes 1997

Published in 1997 by Cedco Publishing Company,
2955 Kerner Blvd, San Rafael, CA 94901.

Produced by Kel Geddes
Color separations by Image Centre
Printed in Hong Kong

ANNE GEDDES ™

is the registered trademark
of The Especially Kids Company Limited

ANNE GEDDES

Anne has been very successful in forming a special relationship with the American public. Appearances on a host of television and radio stations and articles in a range of newspapers and magazines attest to the reputation that this extraordinary Australian-born photographer has achieved with her images.

That unique magic that is the essence of every child is captured beautifully in Anne's exceptional photographs. Nothing says it more perfectly than the images in the Tiny Angels collection.

"I photograph babies, because I love babies." Anne says, "I'm really pleased that people are acknowledging what I do, because what they are really saying is that they love the babies, and with that, they are spreading all this good will."

1998

JANUARY

S	M	T	W	T	F	S
				1	2	3
4	5	6	7	8	9	10
11	12	13	14	15	16	17
18	19	20	21	22	23	24
25	26	27	28	29	30	31

FEBRUARY

S	M	T	W	T	F	S
1	2	3	4	5	6	7
8	9	10	11	12	13	14
15	16	17	18	19	20	21
22	23	24	25	26	27	28

MARCH

S	M	T	W	T	F	S
1	2	3	4	5	6	7
8	9	10	11	12	13	14
15	16	17	18	19	20	21
22	23	24	25	26	27	28
29	30	31				

APRIL

S	M	T	W	T	F	S
			1	2	3	4
5	6	7	8	9	10	11
12	13	14	15	16	17	18
19	20	21	22	23	24	25
26	27	28	29	30		

MAY

S	M	T	W	T	F	S
31					1	2
3	4	5	6	7	8	9
10	11	12	13	14	15	16
17	18	19	20	21	22	23
24	25	26	27	28	29	30

JUNE

S	M	T	W	T	F	S
	1	2	3	4	5	6
7	8	9	10	11	12	13
14	15	16	17	18	19	20
21	22	23	24	25	26	27
28	29	30				

JULY

S	M	T	W	T	F	S
			1	2	3	4
5	6	7	8	9	10	11
12	13	14	15	16	17	18
19	20	21	22	23	24	25
26	27	28	29	30	31	

AUGUST

S	M	T	W	T	F	S
30	31					1
2	3	4	5	6	7	8
9	10	11	12	13	14	15
16	17	18	19	20	21	22
23	24	25	26	27	28	29

SEPTEMBER

S	M	T	W	T	F	S
		1	2	3	4	5
6	7	8	9	10	11	12
13	14	15	16	17	18	19
20	21	22	23	24	25	26
27	28	29	30			

OCTOBER

S	M	T	W	T	F	S
				1	2	3
4	5	6	7	8	9	10
11	12	13	14	15	16	17
18	19	20	21	22	23	24
25	26	27	28	29	30	31

NOVEMBER

S	M	T	W	T	F	S
1	2	3	4	5	6	7
8	9	10	11	12	13	14
15	16	17	18	19	20	21
22	23	24	25	26	27	28
29	30					

DECEMBER

S	M	T	W	T	F	S
		1	2	3	4	5
6	7	8	9	10	11	12
13	14	15	16	17	18	19
20	21	22	23	24	25	26
27	28	29	30	31		

December

SUNDAY 21

Winter Solstice
3:09 PM E.S.T.

Last Quarter

MONDAY 22

TUESDAY 23

Hanukkah
(begins at sunset)

WEDNESDAY 24

THURSDAY 25

Christmas Day

FRIDAY 26

Boxing Day (Canada)

SATURDAY 27

			JANUARY			
S	M	T	W	T	F	S
				1	2	3
4	5	6	7	8	9	10
11	12	13	14	15	16	17
18	19	20	21	22	23	24
25	26	27	28	29	30	31

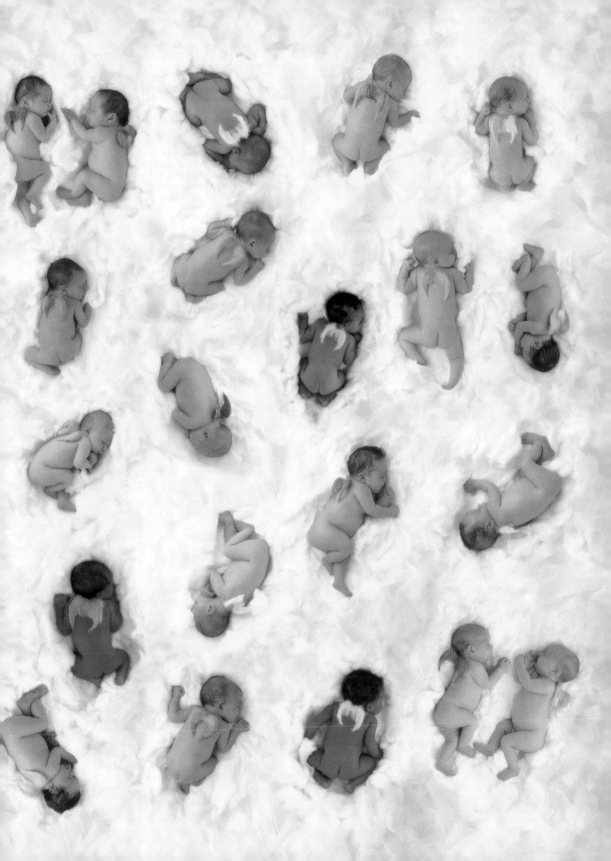

December / January

SUNDAY 28

MONDAY 29

●
New Moon

TUESDAY 30

WEDNESDAY 31

THURSDAY 1 PENNY · WORK.

New Year's Day

FRIDAY 2 PENNY - WORK

SATURDAY 3 PENNY - OFF

			JANUARY			
S	M	T	W	T	F	S
				1	2	3
4	5	6	7	8	9	10
11	12	13	14	15	16	17
18	19	20	21	22	23	24
25	26	27	28	29	30	31

January

SUNDAY 4 PENNY. OFF

MONDAY 5 JOANN - S/p 2000 9-12:30PM CXLD
PENNY. OFF. STAT

◐
First Quarter

TUESDAY 6

WEDNESDAY 7

THURSDAY 8 S.P.
WORK

FRIDAY 9
WORK

SATURDAY 10 BRIDAL FARE '98
OFF

SUNDAY 11   BRIDAL FAIR '98 - OFF

MONDAY 12   JIM OFF.
            ZIG & JOANNE - GRAT MEETING. 2:00PM
○   JOANNE - SICK
Full Moon

TUESDAY 13

WEDNESDAY 14

THURSDAY 15

            DOCTOR'S APPOINTMENT 4:30 PM

FRIDAY 16   DUTY MANAGER.

SATURDAY 17
            BRIDAL FANTASY.

| | | | JANUARY | | | |
S	M	T	W	T	F	S
				1	2	3
4	5	6	7	8	9	10
11	12	13	14	15	16	17
18	19	20	21	22	23	24
25	26	27	28	29	30	31

January

SUNDAY 18

MONDAY 19

Martin Luther King, Jr. Day

TUESDAY 20

◑
Last Quarter

WEDNESDAY 21

MTN TO VALLEY.

THURSDAY 22

FRIDAY 23

CHILI COOKOFF

SATURDAY 24

			JANUARY			
S	M	T	W	T	F	S
				1	2	3
4	5	6	7	8	9	10
11	12	13	14	15	16	17
18	19	20	21	22	23	24
25	26	27	28	29	30	31

January

SUNDAY 25

MONDAY 26   JOANNE - OFF (97' STAT)

TUESDAY 27

WEDNESDAY 28   2:00 PM Acct Meeting

●

New Moon

THURSDAY 29

FRIDAY 30

SATURDAY 31

JANUARY						
S	M	T	W	T	F	S
				1	2	3
4	5	6	7	8	9	10
11	12	13	14	15	16	17
18	19	20	21	22	23	24
25	26	27	28	29	30	31

February

SUNDAY 1

MONDAY 2

TUESDAY 3

◐
First Quarter

WEDNESDAY 4

THURSDAY 5

OFF   4/5 AWARDS

FRIDAY 6

OFF

SATURDAY 7

JOANNE - TRAIN CASHIER

SUNDAY 8   JOANNE - TRAIN CASHIER

MONDAY 9   JIM OFF   - TELL HAZEL !

TUESDAY 10

WEDNESDAY 11

○
Full Moon

THURSDAY 12   PENNY OFF
Lincoln's Birthday   JIM OFF - STAT

FRIDAY 13   JOANNE OFF (FEB 7)
PENNY OFF

SATURDAY 14

St. Valentine's Day   PENNY OFF

FEBRUARY						
S	M	T	W	T	F	S
1	2	3	4	5	6	7
8	9	10	11	12	13	14
15	16	17	18	19	20	21
22	23	24	25	26	27	28

February

SUNDAY 15

PENNY OFF

MONDAY 16
Presidents' Day

JOANNE OFF (FEB 9)
PENNY OFF

TUESDAY 17

PENNY OFF

WEDNESDAY 18

PENNY OFF

THURSDAY 19

ACCT MEETING 2:00 PM
PENNY OFF

◑
Last Quarter

FRIDAY 20

PENNY BACK TO WORK
9:30 STEVENS - DOCTOR'S APPT.

SATURDAY 21

JIM OFF

FEBRUARY						
S	M	T	W	T	F	S
1	2	3	4	5	6	7
8	9	10	11	12	13	14
15	16	17	18	19	20	21
22	23	24	25	26	27	28

February

SUNDAY 22
Washington's Birthday

JIM OFF

MONDAY 23

J SERBA   SP   9-12:30
JIM OFF

PENNY'S PARTY

TUESDAY 24

JIM - REG DAY OFF
3:00 JOANNE'S EVALUATION

WEDNESDAY 25
Ash Wednesday

JIM - REG DAY OFF
PALLISER - DAY AUDIT STAFF

THURSDAY 26

2:00 JEFF (WEDDING PLANS)
1:30 MARION (PASTRIES)

● *New Moon*

FRIDAY 27

SATURDAY 28

FEBRUARY						
S	M	T	W	T	F	S
1	2	3	4	5	6	7
8	9	10	11	12	13	14
15	16	17	18	19	20	21
22	23	24	25	26	27	28

March

SUNDAY 1

MONDAY 2 JOANNE'S EVALUATION

4:00PM JEFF - WEDDING PLANS

TUESDAY 3

WEDNESDAY 4

THURSDAY 5 DAY OFF

◐
First Quarter

FRIDAY 6 JOANNE OFF. - TELL HAZEL
DAY OFF

SATURDAY 7

			MARCH			
S	M	T	W	T	F	S
1	2	3	4	5	6	7
8	9	10	11	12	13	14
15	16	17	18	19	20	21
22	23	24	25	26	27	28
29	30	31				

SUNDAY 8

International Women's Day

MONDAY 9   MARK - MEETING   12:00 PM

TUESDAY 10   M. DUE / J FAHEY   MEETING   1:00 PM .

WEDNESDAY 11   BLOOD WORK - HOSPITAL

THURSDAY 12   TASHA ARRIVES 6:15 BUS
EMPIRE LANMARK (WED)

○
Full Moon

FRIDAY 13   9:00 AM HAIR APPT.

SATURDAY 14
10:00 AM. HAIR APPT

March

SUNDAY 15

MONDAY 16 *Acct Meeting 2:00pm*

TUESDAY 17

St. Patrick's Day

WEDNESDAY 18

THURSDAY 19

FRIDAY 20

Vernal Equinox 2:56 p.m. E.S.T.

SATURDAY 21

Last Quarter

SUNDAY 22

MONDAY 23

TUESDAY 24 Jim L2000   # 8

WEDNESDAY 25

THURSDAY 26

FRIDAY 27 BACK TO WORK
- SYCRONIZE PASSWORDS
- MEETING WITH NANCY- MARRIAGE LICENSE.

● New Moon

SATURDAY 28

MARCH						
S	M	T	W	T	F	S
1	2	3	4	5	6	7
8	9	10	11	12	13	14
15	16	17	18	19	20	21
22	23	24	25	26	27	28
29	30	31				

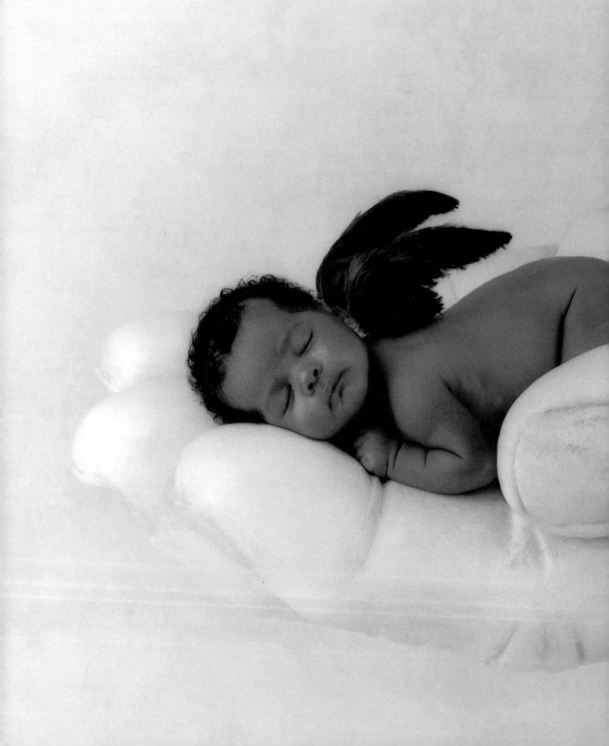

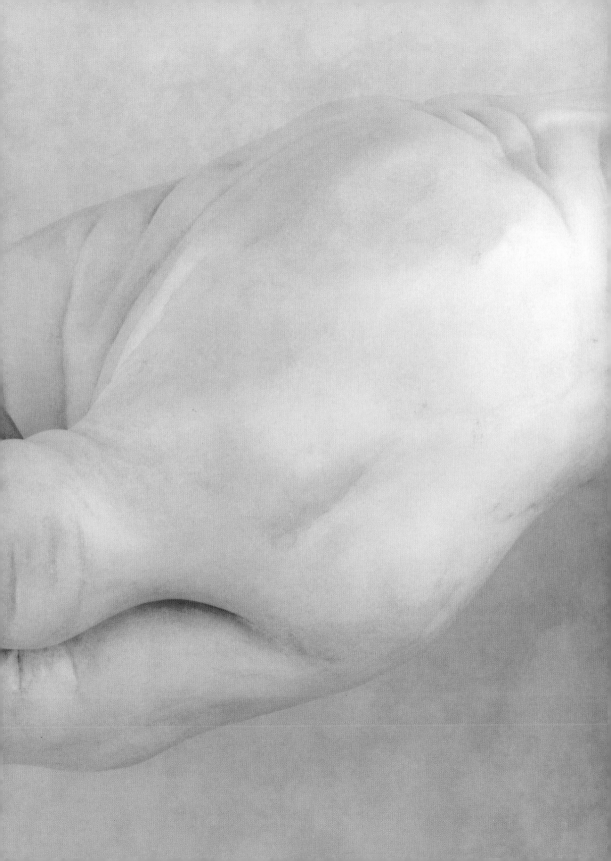

March April

SUNDAY 29

MONDAY 30

— Lunch with Perry.
   Questions
— 2:00 Acct Meeting.

TUESDAY 31

WEDNESDAY 1

THURSDAY 2   Service Plus   T.C.   5:00pm
— Lift Tickets
— Misc.

FRIDAY 3   Lemon B'Day Cake.
— Plants?

◑
First Quarter

SATURDAY 4

			APRIL			
S	M	T	W	T	F	S
			1	2	3	4
5	6	7	8	9	10	11
12	13	14	15	16	17	18
19	20	21	22	23	24	25
26	27	28	29	30		

April

SUNDAY 5

Palm Sunday
Daylight Saving Time begins in U.S.A. (add 1 hour to clock)

JOANNES B'DAY - 24

MONDAY 6

JOANNE OFF — TELL HAZEL
START NEW JOB

G/C

TUESDAY 7

G/C

WEDNESDAY 8

G/C

THURSDAY 9

ACCT

FRIDAY 10

Passover (begins at sunset)
Good Friday

ACCT (.STAT)

SATURDAY 11

○
Full Moon

SUNDAY 12

Easter

MONDAY 13

Easter Monday (Canada)

G/C

TUESDAY 14

G/C

WEDNESDAY 15

G/C

THURSDAY 16   RANDY SYKES - B'DAY.

~~GTE~~ ACCT - DUTY MGR.

FRIDAY 17

G/C

SATURDAY 18

			APRIL			
S	M	T	W	T	F	S
			1	2	3	4
5	6	7	8	9	10	11
12	13	14	15	16	17	18
19	20	21	22	23	24	25
26	27	28	29	30		

April

SUNDAY 19

MONDAY 20

G/C

TUESDAY 21

1ST AID

WEDNESDAY 22

Earth Day

1ST AID

THURSDAY 23

G/C

FRIDAY 24

National Arbor Day

G/C

SATURDAY 25

APRIL						
S	M	T	W	T	F	S
			1	2	3	4
5	6	7	8	9	10	11
12	13	14	15	16	17	18
19	20	21	22	23	24	25
26	27	28	29	30		

April May

SUNDAY 26

●
New Moon

MONDAY 27 JIM CASHABECK · B'DAY.

G/C

TUESDAY 28

G/C

WEDNESDAY 29

G/C

THURSDAY 30

ACCT

FRIDAY 1

ACCT

SATURDAY 2

ACCT

		MAY				
S	M	T	W	T	F	S
31					1	2
3	4	5	6	7	8	9
10	11	12	13	14	15	16
17	18	19	20	21	22	23
24	25	26	27	28	29	30

May

SUNDAY 3

○ OFF

First Quarter

MONDAY 4

~~GOLF CLINIC   7:15 PM. (PAID)~~

OFF

TUESDAY 5

G/C   OVERTIME 3 HOURS

WEDNESDAY 6

CLEAN-UP & B.B.Q. DAY

G/C   LEFT 1/2 EARLY

THURSDAY 7

DENTIST 2:00 PM

FRIDAY 8

SATURDAY 9

SUNDAY 10

Mother's Day

MONDAY 11

○
Full Moon

TUESDAY 12

WEDNESDAY 13

THURSDAY 14

DOCTOR   11:15AM (KONKIN)

FRIDAY 15

SATURDAY 16

JIM HOLIDAYS

			MAY			
S	M	T	W	T	F	S
31					1	2
3	4	5	6	7	8	9
10	11	12	13	14	15	16
17	18	19	20	21	22	23
24	25	26	27	28	29	30

May

SUNDAY 17

MONDAY 18

Victoria Day (Canada)

TUESDAY 19

Last Quarter

WEDNESDAY 20

THURSDAY 21

FRIDAY 22

SATURDAY 23

			MAY			
S	M	T	W	T	F	S
31					1	2
3	4	5	6	7	8	9
10	11	12	13	14	15	16
17	18	19	20	21	22	23
24	25	26	27	28	29	30

May

SUNDAY 24

MONDAY 25

Memorial Day

New Moon

TUESDAY 26

WEDNESDAY 27

THURSDAY 28

Golf Clinic   6:00 PM (PAID)

FRIDAY 29

SATURDAY 30

			MAY			
S	M	T	W	T	F	S
31					1	2
3	4	5	6	7	8	9
10	11	12	13	14	15	16
17	18	19	20	21	22	23
24	25	26	27	28	29	30

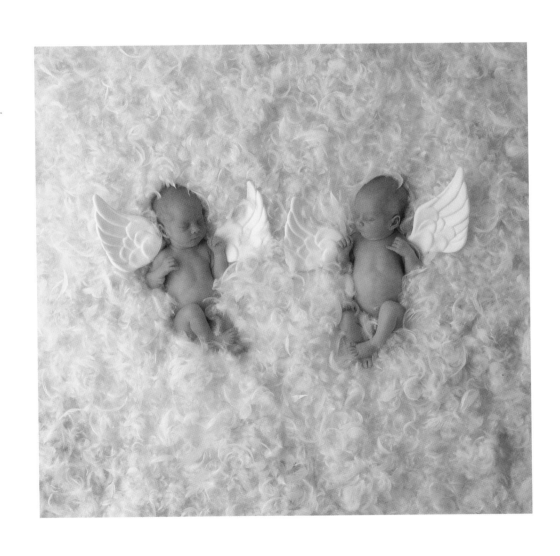

May

June

SUNDAY 31

Pentecost

MONDAY 1

◐
First Quarter

TUESDAY 2

WEDNESDAY 3

THURSDAY 4

FRIDAY 5

SATURDAY 6

SUNDAY 7

MONDAY 8

TUESDAY 9

WEDNESDAY 10

○
Full Moon

THURSDAY 11

HINTON   1:30 PM.
- ULTRA
- 4 BEFORE 1 HOUR.

FRIDAY 12

SATURDAY 13

			JUNE			
S	M	T	W	T	F	S
	1	2	3	4	5	6
7	8	9	10	11	12	13
14	15	16	17	18	19	20
21	22	23	24	25	26	27
28	29	30				

June

SUNDAY 14

Flag Day

MONDAY 15 PROVERA · DAY 1

TUESDAY 16   DAY 2

WEDNESDAY 17   DAY 3

◑ *Last Quarter* ♡

THURSDAY 18   DAY 4

STARTED CYCLE · PM ·

FRIDAY 19   DAY 5

SATURDAY 20   DAY 6

SUNDAY 21   DAY 7

Summer Solstice 10:04 a.m. E.D.T
Father's Day

MONDAY 22   HOLIDAYS START.   DAY 8

TUESDAY 23   STAFF MEETS MGMT.   DAY 9

●
New Moon

WEDNESDAY 24   DAY 10

St. Jean Baptiste Day (Quebec)

♡

THURSDAY 25

FRIDAY 26

SATURDAY 27

♡

			JUNE			
S	M	T	W	T	F	S
	1	2	3	4	5	6
7	8	9	10	11	12	13
14	15	16	17	18	19	20
21	22	23	24	25	26	27
28	29	30				

June / *July*

SUNDAY 28

MONDAY 29

♡

TUESDAY 30

WEDNESDAY 1

Canada Day (Canada)

◗ *First Quarter*

WORKED 5 HOURS

THURSDAY 2

BACK TO WORK

FRIDAY 3

SATURDAY 4

Independence Day

JULY						
S	M	T	W	T	F	S
			1	2	3	4
5	6	7	8	9	10	11
12	13	14	15	16	17	18
19	20	21	22	23	24	25
26	27	28	29	30	31	

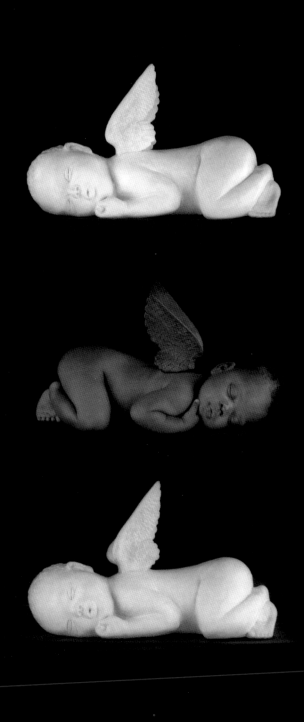

July

SUNDAY 5

MONDAY 6

TUESDAY 7

WEDNESDAY 8

THURSDAY 9

○
Full Moon   HARASSMENT PREVENTION   1-4 PM

FRIDAY 10

SATURDAY 11

SUNDAY 12

MONDAY 13

TUESDAY 14   *TALK W/ PERRY*

WEDNESDAY 15

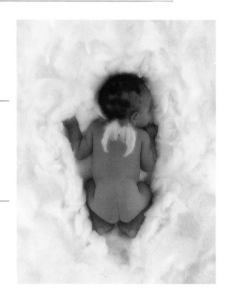

THURSDAY 16

Last Quarter

FRIDAY 17

SATURDAY 18

			JULY			
S	M	T	W	T	F	S
			1	2	3	4
5	6	7	8	9	10	11
12	13	14	15	16	17	18
19	20	21	22	23	24	25
26	27	28	29	30	31	

July

SUNDAY 19

MONDAY 20

TUESDAY 21

WEDNESDAY 22

THURSDAY 23

New Moon

FRIDAY 24

SATURDAY 25

			JULY			
S	M	T	W	T	F	S
			1	2	3	4
5	6	7	8	9	10	11
12	13	14	15	16	17	18
19	20	21	22	23	24	25
26	27	28	29	30	31	

July / August

SUNDAY 26

MONDAY 27

TUESDAY 28

WEDNESDAY 29

THURSDAY 30   KANANASKIS

⋆ 1 STARTED CYCLE · PM .
     ON OWN

FRIDAY 31

◑ 2
First Quarter

SATURDAY 1

3

		AUGUST				
S	M	T	W	T	F	S
30	31					1
2	3	4	5	6	7	8
9	10	11	12	13	14	15
16	17	18	19	20	21	22
23	24	25	26	27	28	29

August

SUNDAY 2

4

MONDAY 3

5

TUESDAY 4

WEDNESDAY 5   7-3:30

THURSDAY 6   OFF

FRIDAY 7   OFF

○
Full Moon

SATURDAY 8   12-8:30

SUNDAY 9   12 - 8:30

♡

MONDAY 10   9 - 5:30

TUESDAY 11   WANDA'S   B'DAY.   9 - 5:30

WEDNESDAY 12   7 - 3:30

THURSDAY 13   OFF

◑
Last Quarter

FRIDAY 14   OFF

SATURDAY 15   AUGUST 12 - 8:30

S	M	T	W	T	F	S
30	31					1
2	3	4	5	6	7	8
9	10	11	12	13	14	15
16	17	18	19	20	21	22
23	24	25	26	27	28	29

August

SUNDAY 16   9-5:30

MONDAY 17   7 - 12:30
RAINING

TUESDAY 18   9-5:30 ?

WEDNESDAY 19   7:30

THURSDAY 20   OFF

FRIDAY 21   OFF

●
New Moon

SATURDAY 22   Ⓥ

BARB & GARY'S 25TH
ANNIVERSARY - CANWOOD

SUNDAY 23　　　　　　　　　　　　　　　　V

MONDAY 24　　　　　　　　　　　　　　　V

TUESDAY 25　　　　　　　　　　　　　　V

WEDNESDAY 26　　　　　　　　　　　　X

THURSDAY 27　　　　　　　　　　　OFF

FRIDAY 28　　　　　　　　　　　　OFF

SATURDAY 29　　　　　　　　　　　AUGUST　OFF

S	M	T	W	T	F	S
30	31					1
2	3	4	5	6	7	8
9	10	11	12	13	14	15
16	17	18	19	20	21	22
23	24	25	26	27	28	29

August   September

SUNDAY **30**   12-8

* STARTED CYCLE AM
◑ **1** ON OWN
First Quarter

MONDAY **31**   12-8

2

TUESDAY **1**   7-3:30

3

WEDNESDAY **2** SUPER SEVERE HEADACHE   7-3:30

4

THURSDAY **3**   OFF

5

FRIDAY **4**   OFF

6

SATURDAY **5**   DAY OWED

		SEPTEMBER				
S	M	T	W	T	F	S
		1	2	3	4	5
6	7	8	9	10	11	12
13	14	15	16	17	18	19
20	21	22	23	24	25	26
27	28	29	30			

7

September

SUNDAY 6

DAY OWED.

○ ❀
Full Moon

MONDAY 7

Labor Day

8 ← 5:30

9

TUESDAY 8

7:45 - 5:15

10

WEDNESDAY 9

7:45 - 4:15

1ST DAY OF AEROBICS.

THURSDAY 10

X

FRIDAY 11

X

♡

SATURDAY 12

11 - 7:30

◑ ♡
Last Quarter

SEPTEMBER						
S	M	T	W	T	F	S
		1	2	3	4	5
6	7	8	9	10	11	12
13	14	15	16	17	18	19
20	21	22	23	24	25	26
27	28	29	30			

September

SUNDAY 13

Grandparents' Day

11-7:30

MONDAY 14

9-5:30

TUESDAY 15

9-5:30

WEDNESDAY 16

8-4:30

THURSDAY 17   LAKE LOUISE

X

FRIDAY 18

X

SATURDAY 19

11:30-7:30

SUNDAY 20

Rosh Hashanah (begins at sunset)

●

New Moon

11·30–7·30

MONDAY 21

8 – 4:30

TUESDAY 22

8 – 4:30

WEDNESDAY 23

Autumnal Equinox 1:39 a.m. E.D.T.

8 – 4:30

THURSDAY 24

FRIDAY 25

SATURDAY 26

11·30–6·30

SEPTEMBER						
S	M	T	W	T	F	S
		1	2	3	4	5
6	7	8	9	10	11	12
13	14	15	16	17	18	19
20	21	22	23	24	25	26
27	28	29	30			

September/
October

11·30 —

SUNDAY 27

MONDAY 28   8:00 – 4:30

◑
First Quarter

TUESDAY 29   8:00 – 4:30
Yom Kippur (begins at sunset)

STARTED ON OWN
DAY 1

WEDNESDAY 30   8:00 – 5:00

2

THURSDAY 1   X 2hrs OT

3

FRIDAY 2   X

4

SATURDAY 3

		OCTOBER				
S	M	T	W	T	F	S
				1	2	3
4	5	6	7	8	9	10
11	12	13	14	15	16	17
18	19	20	21	22	23	24
25	26	27	28	29	30	31

5

11 – 7:00

October

SUNDAY 4   OFF

6

MONDAY 5   9–5:30

○ 7
Full Moon

TUESDAY 6 ♡   9–5:15

8

WEDNESDAY 7 ♡   9–5:30

9

THURSDAY 8   OFF

10

FRIDAY 9   OFF

11

SATURDAY 10

			OCTOBER			
S	M	T	W	T	F	S
				1	2	3
4	5	6	7	8	9	10
11	12	13	14	15	16	17
18	19	20	21	22	23	24
25	26	27	28	29	30	31

12

10 — 5:45

SUNDAY 11

WANDA'S - SUPPER
- SALAD.

13

MONDAY 12

9 - 5

♡

◑ 14
Last Quarter

TUESDAY 13

STAFF GOLF TOURNEY.
OFF

WEDNESDAY 14

9 - 5

THURSDAY 15

P.G.

FRIDAY 16 ♡

P.G.

SATURDAY 17

11 - 7

♡

October

SUNDAY 18

HSKP   9-4:15

2 hrs · Starter's Hut

MONDAY 19

3 hrs. - CALL IN ?

TUESDAY 20

● *New Moon*

8 - 4:30   XMAS

WEDNESDAY 21

8 - 4:30   XMAS

THURSDAY 22

8 - 4:30   XMAS

FRIDAY 23

8 - 4:30   XMAS

SATURDAY 24

♡

OFF

OCTOBER						
S	M	T	W	T	F	S
					1	2	3
4	5	6	7	8	9	10
11	12	13	14	15	16	17
18	19	20	21	22	23	24
25	26	27	28	29	30	31

October

SUNDAY 25   OFF

Daylight Saving Time ends in U.S.A. (subtract 1 hour from clock)

♡

MONDAY 26   8-4:30   HOT

TUESDAY 27   8-4:30   HOT

WEDNESDAY 28   8-4:30   XMAS LIGHTS

◑

First Quarter

THURSDAY 29   8-4:30   G/C
D.S. FAREWELL

FRIDAY 30   8-4:30   SALES

B'DAY.

SATURDAY 31

Halloween

OCTOBER						
S	M	T	W	T	F	S
				1	2	3
4	5	6	7	8	9	10
11	12	13	14	15	16	17
18	19	20	21	22	23	24
25	26	27	28	29	30	31

November

SUNDAY 1

EDMONTON

♡

MONDAY 2

EDMONTON

♡

TUESDAY 3

Election Day

~~EDMONTON~~
CRAZY JANE

♡

WEDNESDAY 4

○
Full Moon

THURSDAY 5

FRIDAY 6

SATURDAY 7

STARTED ON OWN
VERY BLOATED · PAIN.

SUNDAY 8

MONDAY 9

TUESDAY 10

Last Quarter

WEDNESDAY 11

Veterans Day
Remembrance Day (Canada)

THURSDAY 12

FRIDAY 13

SATURDAY 14

NOVEMBER						
S	M	T	W	T	F	S
1	2	3	4	5	6	7
8	9	10	11	12	13	14
15	16	17	18	19	20	21
22	23	24	25	26	27	28
29	30					

November

SUNDAY 15

MONDAY 16

TUESDAY 17

WEDNESDAY 18

●

New Moon

THURSDAY 19

HOME AGAIN

FRIDAY 20

SATURDAY 21

SUNDAY 22   WANDA LEAVES

MONDAY 23

TUESDAY 24

WEDNESDAY 25

THURSDAY 26

Thanksgiving Day

◑
First Quarter

FRIDAY 27

SATURDAY 28

NOVEMBER						
S	M	T	W	T	F	S
1	2	3	4	5	6	7
8	9	10	11	12	13	14
15	16	17	18	19	20	21
22	23	24	25	26	27	28
29	30					

November December

SUNDAY 29

MONDAY 30

TUESDAY 1

WEDNESDAY 2

THURSDAY 3

○
Full Moon

FRIDAY 4

SATURDAY 5

DECEMBER						
S	M	T	W	T	F	S
		1	2	3	4	5
6	7	8	9	10	11	12
13	14	15	16	17	18	19
20	21	22	23	24	25	26
27	28	29	30	31		

December

SUNDAY 6 RCMP Party

MONDAY 7

TUESDAY 8

WEDNESDAY 9 PEP's PARTY.

THURSDAY 10

◑
Last Quarter

FRIDAY 11 PATTI'S PARTY.

SATURDAY 12 FIRE PARTY

DECEMBER						
S	M	T	W	T	F	S
		1	2	3	4	5
6	7	8	9	10	11	12
13	14	15	16	17	18	19
20	21	22	23	24	25	26
27	28	29	30	31		

SUNDAY 13

Hanukkah (begins at sunset)

MONDAY 14

TUESDAY 15

WEDNESDAY 16

THURSDAY 17

FRIDAY 18

New Moon

SATURDAY 19

December

SUNDAY 20

MONDAY 21

Winter Solstice 8:58 p.m. E.S.T.

TUESDAY 22

WEDNESDAY 23

THURSDAY 24

FRIDAY 25

Christmas Day

SATURDAY 26

Boxing Day (Canada)

◗

First Quarter

			DECEMBER			
S	M	T	W	T	F	S
		1	2	3	4	5
6	7	8	9	10	11	12
13	14	15	16	17	18	19
20	21	22	23	24	25	26
27	28	29	30	31		

December / January

SUNDAY 27

MONDAY 28

Holidays · Mexico

TUESDAY 29

WEDNESDAY 30

THURSDAY 31

FRIDAY 1

New Year's Day

SATURDAY 2

			JANUARY			
S	M	T	W	T	F	S
31					1	2
3	4	5	6	7	8	9
10	11	12	13	14	15	16
17	18	19	20	21	22	23
24	25	26	27	28	29	30

1999

JANUARY
```
 S  M  T  W  T  F  S
31              1  2
 3  4  5  6  7  8  9
10 11 12 13 14 15 16
17 18 19 20 21 22 23
24 25 26 27 28 29 30
```

FEBRUARY
```
 S  M  T  W  T  F  S
    1  2  3  4  5  6
 7  8  9 10 11 12 13
14 15 16 17 18 19 20
21 22 23 24 25 26 27
28
```

MARCH
```
 S  M  T  W  T  F  S
    1  2  3  4  5  6
 7  8  9 10 11 12 13
14 15 16 17 18 19 20
21 22 23 24 25 26 27
28 29 30 31
```

APRIL
```
 S  M  T  W  T  F  S
             1  2  3
 4  5  6  7  8  9 10
11 12 13 14 15 16 17
18 19 20 21 22 23 24
25 26 27 28 29 30
```

MAY
```
 S  M  T  W  T  F  S
30 31              1
 2  3  4  5  6  7  8
 9 10 11 12 13 14 15
16 17 18 19 20 21 22
23 24 25 26 27 28 29
```

JUNE
```
 S  M  T  W  T  F  S
       1  2  3  4  5
 6  7  8  9 10 11 12
13 14 15 16 17 18 19
20 21 22 23 24 25 26
27 28 29 30
```

JULY
```
 S  M  T  W  T  F  S
             1  2  3
 4  5  6  7  8  9 10
11 12 13 14 15 16 17
18 19 20 21 22 23 24
25 26 27 28 29 30 31
```

AUGUST
```
 S  M  T  W  T  F  S
 1  2  3  4  5  6  7
 8  9 10 11 12 13 14
15 16 17 18 19 20 21
22 23 24 25 26 27 28
29 30 31
```

SEPTEMBER
```
 S  M  T  W  T  F  S
          1  2  3  4
 5  6  7  8  9 10 11
12 13 14 15 16 17 18
19 20 21 22 23 24 25
26 27 28 29 30
```

OCTOBER
```
 S  M  T  W  T  F  S
31              1  2
 3  4  5  6  7  8  9
10 11 12 13 14 15 16
17 18 19 20 21 22 23
24 25 26 27 28 29 30
```

NOVEMBER
```
 S  M  T  W  T  F  S
    1  2  3  4  5  6
 7  8  9 10 11 12 13
14 15 16 17 18 19 20
21 22 23 24 25 26 27
28 29 30
```

DECEMBER
```
 S  M  T  W  T  F  S
          1  2  3  4
 5  6  7  8  9 10 11
12 13 14 15 16 17 18
19 20 21 22 23 24 25
26 27 28 29 30 31
```

2000

JANUARY
```
 S  M  T  W  T  F  S
30 31              1
 2  3  4  5  6  7  8
 9 10 11 12 13 14 15
16 17 18 19 20 21 22
23 24 25 26 27 28 29
```

FEBRUARY
```
 S  M  T  W  T  F  S
       1  2  3  4  5
 6  7  8  9 10 11 12
13 14 15 16 17 18 19
20 21 22 23 24 25 26
27 28 29
```

MARCH
```
 S  M  T  W  T  F  S
          1  2  3  4
 5  6  7  8  9 10 11
12 13 14 15 16 17 18
19 20 21 22 23 24 25
26 27 28 29 30 31
```

APRIL
```
 S  M  T  W  T  F  S
30                 1
 2  3  4  5  6  7  8
 9 10 11 12 13 14 15
16 17 18 19 20 21 22
23 24 25 26 27 28 29
```

MAY
```
 S  M  T  W  T  F  S
    1  2  3  4  5  6
 7  8  9 10 11 12 13
14 15 16 17 18 19 20
21 22 23 24 25 26 27
28 29 30 31
```

JUNE
```
 S  M  T  W  T  F  S
             1  2  3
 4  5  6  7  8  9 10
11 12 13 14 15 16 17
18 19 20 21 22 23 24
25 26 27 28 29 30
```

JULY
```
 S  M  T  W  T  F  S
30 31              1
 2  3  4  5  6  7  8
 9 10 11 12 13 14 15
16 17 18 19 20 21 22
23 24 25 26 27 28 29
```

AUGUST
```
 S  M  T  W  T  F  S
       1  2  3  4  5
 6  7  8  9 10 11 12
13 14 15 16 17 18 19
20 21 22 23 24 25 26
27 28 29 30 31
```

SEPTEMBER
```
 S  M  T  W  T  F  S
             1  2
 3  4  5  6  7  8  9
10 11 12 13 14 15 16
17 18 19 20 21 22 23
24 25 26 27 28 29 30
```

OCTOBER
```
 S  M  T  W  T  F  S
 1  2  3  4  5  6  7
 8  9 10 11 12 13 14
15 16 17 18 19 20 21
22 23 24 25 26 27 28
29 30 31
```

NOVEMBER
```
 S  M  T  W  T  F  S
          1  2  3  4
 5  6  7  8  9 10 11
12 13 14 15 16 17 18
19 20 21 22 23 24 25
26 27 28 29 30
```

DECEMBER
```
 S  M  T  W  T  F  S
31              1  2
 3  4  5  6  7  8  9
10 11 12 13 14 15 16
17 18 19 20 21 22 23
24 25 26 27 28 29 30
```

2001

JANUARY
```
 S  M  T  W  T  F  S
    1  2  3  4  5  6
 7  8  9 10 11 12 13
14 15 16 17 18 19 20
21 22 23 24 25 26 27
28 29 30 31
```

FEBRUARY
```
 S  M  T  W  T  F  S
             1  2  3
 4  5  6  7  8  9 10
11 12 13 14 15 16 17
18 19 20 21 22 23 24
25 26 27 28
```

MARCH
```
 S  M  T  W  T  F  S
             1  2  3
 4  5  6  7  8  9 10
11 12 13 14 15 16 17
18 19 20 21 22 23 24
25 26 27 28 29 30 31
```

APRIL
```
 S  M  T  W  T  F  S
 1  2  3  4  5  6  7
 8  9 10 11 12 13 14
15 16 17 18 19 20 21
22 23 24 25 26 27 28
29 30
```

MAY
```
 S  M  T  W  T  F  S
       1  2  3  4  5
 6  7  8  9 10 11 12
13 14 15 16 17 18 19
20 21 22 23 24 25 26
27 28 29 30 31
```

JUNE
```
 S  M  T  W  T  F  S
                1  2
 3  4  5  6  7  8  9
10 11 12 13 14 15 16
17 18 19 20 21 22 23
24 25 26 27 28 29 30
```

JULY
```
 S  M  T  W  T  F  S
 1  2  3  4  5  6  7
 8  9 10 11 12 13 14
15 16 17 18 19 20 21
22 23 24 25 26 27 28
29 30 31
```

AUGUST
```
 S  M  T  W  T  F  S
          1  2  3  4
 5  6  7  8  9 10 11
12 13 14 15 16 17 18
19 20 21 22 23 24 25
26 27 28 29 30 31
```

SEPTEMBER
```
 S  M  T  W  T  F  S
30                 1
 2  3  4  5  6  7  8
 9 10 11 12 13 14 15
16 17 18 19 20 21 22
23 24 25 26 27 28 29
```

OCTOBER
```
 S  M  T  W  T  F  S
    1  2  3  4  5  6
 7  8  9 10 11 12 13
14 15 16 17 18 19 20
21 22 23 24 25 26 27
28 29 30 31
```

NOVEMBER
```
 S  M  T  W  T  F  S
             1  2  3
 4  5  6  7  8  9 10
11 12 13 14 15 16 17
18 19 20 21 22 23 24
25 26 27 28 29 30
```

DECEMBER
```
 S  M  T  W  T  F  S
30 31              1
 2  3  4  5  6  7  8
 9 10 11 12 13 14 15
16 17 18 19 20 21 22
23 24 25 26 27 28 29
```